KEEPING
GUINEA
FOWL

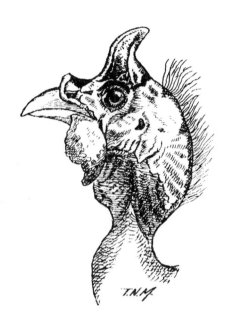

Books for the Smallholder or Fancier

The publishers have many books on the commercial or hobby aspects of keeping poultry-- fowls, bantams; also pigeons, rabbits, ducks, geese, turkeys, guinea fowl, and other stock.

Readers wanting information on these subjects, as well as on cage and aviary birds, should write for details.

KEEPING

GUINEA

FOWL

JOHN BUTLER

Beech Publishing House
Station Yard
Elsted Marsh
Midhurst
West Sussex GU29 OJT

ISBN 1-85736-332-9
First published 1994
Second Edition 1997
New Impression 2,000

British Library Cataloguing-in-Publication Data
A catalogue record for this book is available from the British Library.

Published in conjunction with
the World Bantam & Poultry Society

Beech Publishing House
Station Yard
Elsted Marsh
Midhurst
West Sussex GU29 OJT

CONTENTS

FOREWORD

This book is intended as a guide to keeping the common guinea fowl as a hobby or as the basis of a commercial venture. They are easy to manage and breed with, so they are a suitable type of bird to keep in rural surroundings.

Their main drawback is the shrieking cries made when strangers arrive. They are therefore excellent 'watchdogs', but, because of the cry, are not really suitable for keeping in a community that are not accustomed to the normal sounds of the country .

Sadly even the crow of the rooster, our heralder of the morning's arrival, is not regarded with favour by the town dwellers who decide they would like to live in the country!

The text has been kept concise yet comprehensive enough to cover most needs.

JB   August, 2000

The Vulterine Guinea Fowl
Kept as an Exotic Species and therefore quite rare.
This book is concerned with the common, helmeted variety.

Guinea Fowl and Chicks.

Guinea Fowl: different colours

Old English Game Chicks recently hatched; notice stripe down back.

Guinea Fowl Chicks Hatching

Chicks at Different Stages

1

WHAT ARE GUINEA FOWL ?

Guinea fowl are part of the **order** of birds known as **Galliformes**. This includes a diverse range of quite well known families which include:

1. Pheasants and quails (including Jungle fowl and Peafowl);
2. Turkeys;
3. Grouse.

Each contains a number of species and comes under a family name (eg, *Phasiandiae* for the Pheasant family). The Guinea Fowl come within the family *Numididae* and there are four genera and seven species. The four genera are:

1. *Acryllium;*
2. *Agelastes;*
3. *Guttera;*
4. *Numida.*

The seven species are divided into sub-species making around 40 in total. Some confusion exists on the exact terminology so this figure may have to be adjusted slightly to allow for overlap. The most common is the helmeted and there are over 20 sub-species. The main or nominate species is *meleagris.*

Game Birds

Guinea fowl are generally regarded as 'game birds' and in size come within a range of 43 to 75cm (17 to 30in.). They tend to be fairly compact, yet heavy in relation to size and are robust and hardy. The head tends to be smallish and is generally helmeted or is of a distinctive colour. Some have crests.

Distribution

They originate from Africa and some are quite rare in the wild, whereas others have been domesticated since around the 4th century BC; in other words, they have been kept for around 4,000 years. Illustrations of Guinea Fowl are to be found on the inner walls of the pyramids.

Crested and Helmeted (Common) Guinea Fowl.

History

As noted, Guinea fowl have a very long history of domestication. It was known to the Greeks and Romans. The Greeks gave it the name **Meleagris.** According to ancient legend, after the death of Meleager, his sisters, in mourning, were turned into birds which had their feathers sprinkled with teardrops. These birds were called **Meleagrides** (plural of *Meleagris*).

Many old records and books mention the existence of Guinea fowl. Famous writers which have mentioned them are Aristotle, Pliny, Collumella (an ancient Roman writer) and Varro. Whether the birds were *wide spread* in Greece is difficult to establish.

The introduction into Britain came much later, possibly in the seventeenth century, but were not extensively known until a century later. A famous feast organized by Archbishop Nevill, in the reign of Edward IV, did not include Guinea fowl. Other sources list Peafowl, but not Guinea fowl; for example, the *Household Book* of Henry VIII and a similar book by the Duke of Northumberland (1512). In modern times, birds are now kept on a national basis.

The birds reached America around the same

time as the European imports. In the USA there is a considerable market, although not as large as 50 years ago.

Birds in Captivity

From what has been stated it should be apparent that there are two distinct types of Guinea fowl kept in captivity:

1. *Domesticated or common Guinea fowl.*
(Helmeted Guinea Fowl)

These are *Numida meleagris* or a variation of that species. Just as the Jungle Fowl were the originators of our domestic fowl then we must assume that the wild species were the forerunners of our domesticated Guinea fowl. Nowadays, as will be shown in the next chapter, there are very many hybrids (birds selected and bred for commercial purposes) and mutations (colours that arise by accident and are then bred from).

2. *Rarer Species kept in Zoos and bird gardens.*

Birds like the Crested Guinea fowl or the Vulturine Guinea fowl are kept out of interest, possibly as part of a conservation programme. This is an important function, but should be left to experts. In any event the price of some of the species is quite high and could not be afforded by the farmer or general bird-keeper.

Scope of this Book

The main concern in this book are the domesticated species. The methods employed, feeding, management and other aspects are examined.

In France the commercialization of Guinea fowl is on a very large scale and in Britain attempts are being made to expand the market which at present is limited because it is a bird which is not fully appreciated as a source of food. Indeed, it must be recognized that at present it is primarily an alternative to other game birds such as pheasant, which has a limited market anyway.

With proper publicity and marketing there is considerable scope for making Guinea fowl more widely accepted. Sales in super-stores are an obvious area of expansion.

2
THE
DOMESTICATED SPECIES

COMMON GUINEA FOWL

The common Guinea Fowl may be kept running free in fields, orchards or other ranges, in pens, or in poultry cages designed for laying hens. The **intensive** methods may include deep litter, cages, or outside pens with a very high occupation rate per square metre.

In the wild, Guinea Fowl may lay about 20 eggs per annum, but in domestic surroundings about 80 eggs may be possible.

Colours

Guinea Fowl are a mixture of grey and purple with speckles covering most of the body. Over many years of breeding many new colours have emerged, thus making them more attractive. There are:

1. **Common Grey or Pearl Grey**
2. **White**
3. **Lavender**
4. **Splashed or Pied**
5. **Violet or Royal Purple**

6. **Blues (various combinations)**
7. **Chamois which are a sort of fawn with spots**
8. **Tan or Dark Fawn**

There are also variations of these main varieties. Once a hybrid is in existence it becomes an easy matter to produce other off-colours.

The colour of the standard type may be seen from the illustration at the front of the book. It will be seen that the predominant colour is a bluish grey with speckles or spots, the larger ones being on the breast.

More Colour Details

The colours are predominantly a mixture of greys, purples, whites and blues. The mixture varies according to the specific colour pattern. Thus:

1. Pearl Greys

This is a grey bird with a purple hue and is sprinkled with regular spots all over its body. There is a sort of lavender shade on the neck.

2. White

As indicated by the name, this mutation is entirely white with some having a speck of black on the neck. The skin is also a light colour - pinkish- as would be expected for any bird having white plumage.

3. Lavender

The lavender is a lighter grey than the Common

Grey with the usual white spots. It is the resemblance to lavender or lilac which gives it its name.

4. Splashed or Pied

These are a haphazard mixture of colour which generally appear in any poultry which are blue or black plumed. The basic colour is not produced in full but, instead, comes in a diluted form. The lack of pigmentation comes out in the "splashes". In some mutations the birds have white breasts and flight feathers and the remainder is normal grey.

Where the marking is even, i.e.: **regular** white spots or markings, then an apt description is "Pied".

5. Violet or Royal Purple

These are a dark colour with a purple or violet hue. Once seen it cannot be mistaken, such is the striking colour. Because of the double density of colour the speckles may be missing from the wings or atleast very subdued.

6. Blues

This tends to be a dark, slate blue colour and the number of speckles or spots varies, depending upon the density of the blue.

7. Chamois

This is a light fawn, sometimes with a yellow tinge. Occasionally they may be a creamy colour. The spots tend to be faint simply because there is little contrast.

8. Tan or Dark Fawn

With this mutation the colour tends to be darker than the Chamois and may not have spots, although some specimens do have them.

Description

The Guinea Fowl is a 'gamey' type bird which weighs around 3.50 to about 4.00lb (2kilos) and is naturally plump and rounded.

The **body** is at an angle so that the short tail almost rests on the ground. The **wings** are large and are carried around the body. The **breast** is full and rounded. As a consequence the **back** is broad.

The **legs** are short with little thigh visible.

The **head** is a remarkable feature and consists of a whitish section (kid-like), devoid of feathers, and this is topped with a horn-like helmet, reddish in colour, and below the white section there are wattles which are red.

The **standard colour** is Pearl Grey, noted above, but there are now many mutations or non-standard colours which have aroused a great deal of interest.

Like all bird descriptions it does not do justice to the bird itself which must be seen to be appreciated. *See also page 12 where a suggested standard is given.*

"Tear-Dropped" Feather

Short Neck

Head with Helmet

Broad Breast

Body at an Angle

Legs Short

Features of the Common Guinea Fowl

In the wild many variations occur in the common or helmeted type.

A STANDARD FOR GUINEA FOWL

Various attempts have been made to give a standard description for Guinea Fowl, but, since they are rarely shown, not much progress has been made. Matters which require attention when establishing an "ideal" bird are as follows:

1. **Size**: Cock 4lb; Hen $3^1/_2$ lb. Young adult birds would be slightly less.

2. **Carriage**: Upright, compact body with short legs, coloured brown and orange. The back is relatively broad and breast broad and full.

3. **Head**: Wedge–shaped head with helmet which is curved upwards from the beak to an abrupt step at the back of the head. Gills or wattles which curve from the beak to the front of the neck. The eyes should be full and round, bright and alert; colour, dark brown.

4. **Feathering**: Well feathered, quite tight, with a plentiful layer of fluff under the feathers. Colours should conform with the descriptions given earlier, although, strictly speaking, only the **Pearl Grey** can be regarded as a standard type. Therefore, normal colour should be viewed as the Grey and any variation would call for disqualification. White features or blotches of white or other colour would call for disqualification.

5. **Wings and Tail**: The tail should be carried low in line with the body and fairly short. Wings should be strong, large and carried horizontally.

Differences in Sexes

The female is difficult to distinguish form the male. The male has a stronger head and fuller face, with longer wattles. There is also a difference in the call; females have a two-syllable call compared with the single-syllable call of the male.

Experienced poultry keepers should be able to distinguish the sexes by handling. Laying hens will have a gap between the pelvic bones of two or three fingers where the "opening" has developed to allow the egg to emerge.

In addition, examination of the cloaca by gently pressing each side should reveal a tongue-like appendage which is the sign indicating the male. Females do not have this appendage. This sexing may be done from around 6 months old.

With commercial Guinea Fowl farming, the process of spotting males will be essential. With cage organisations, artificial insemination would be practised. The cocks are "milked" by holding each bird and massaging the abdomen and, holding the copulatory tongue, the semen is extracted.

Usually two operators are required. The semen may be taken two or three times per week. A glass tube is used to collect the drops of semen.

Behaviour

Guinea fowl are aggressive creatures who will live in peace only if they are kept away from other poultry. They prefer to run wild in the farmyard or in an orchard or paddock. A flock I kept in Scotland would roam all day across the fields and in the woodland, but come back in the evening to roost in the trees at the side of the house. They were certainly fully domesticated, but only on their terms. In the mornings and evenings they looked for the mixed corn or layers' pellets and then went away to forage or to perch.

Some breeders have managed to make them fully domesticated to the extent of getting them to mix with other farmyard fowl. This state is more easily accomplished if the chicks (known as keats) are hatched by broody hens; the keets then follow the hen and accept going into the poultry house more readily. They are natural foragers and, as a result, in the milder months, will eat insects and other natural foods, thus to a large extent, keeping themselves.

The call of the Guinea fowl is quite pronounced and their shrieks will deter anyone coming on to premises. As a result they are often kept as watch dogs or as night alarms. Because they have a relatively lightly framed body the Guinea fowl can fly quite easily into the trees. This means that no special housing is required, but beware of foxes because Reynard seems partial to the game flavour of our plump friends. Indeed, some years ago, because of stealing of Old English Game, a pen of Guinea fowl were purchased and placed in a corner pen to act as watch dogs, a task they carried out with much enthusiasm. Alas, the noise was heard by a fox who burrowed under the fence of wire netting and he was able to capture the lot because they were in an enclosed situation.

Reports have been seen that suggests that Guinea fowl have attacked foxes, but we have no experience of this phenomena and would rather doubt its veracity. Undoubtedly, male Guineas can be very aggressive, but when it is known that foxes take geese and turkeys, the smaller bird would have little scope to defend itself. The fact remains that they are very useful birds to have on a small holding or farm which give a built-in system of protection, as well as them being very useful on economic grounds, covered in the next section.

Advantages of Guinea Fowl

The merits of Guinea Fowl have been discussed at length by various authors; in summary form they are as follows:

1. Provide a warning system.
The call has been referred to as a "Come Back" cry and is most unnerving being a series of loud shrieks.

2. Can run free in woodland or coverts (i.e. thicket hiding birds such as Game).

This is a state resembling the wild and will produce naturally reared birds, but they will tend to be wild and may be poached just like pheasants.

3. Being great foragers they will find much of their food.

This means they help to eliminate many insect pests. Constantly on the move they seek out titbits and consume them greedily. This means a relatively low food bill. However, if kept intensively the total food must be given.

4. Hardy and resistant to disease.
Since they will thrive in rather 'rough' conditions the birds have developed a resistance to many of the diseases which affect normal, commercial poultry.

5. Regular demand for birds in restaurants.

This potential has not been exploited fully, but once a market is established in an area it can be developed further.

6. In size, birds reach about 3lb which is ideal for two people or a small family.

The size normally achieved is the ideal for one meal and no left-overs. Obviously, for big events more birds will be used.

Disadvantages

1. Rather noisy and tend to be wild.

This disadvantage can be reduced by taming the birds from the start. Ideally, eggs should be purchased and hatched under a broody hen and the chicks reared in reasonably enclosed surroundings; try to get them to go indoors at night and sleep with the surrogate mother and her behaviour should imprint itself on her young Guineas.

2. Can be rather vicious to other birds.

Running with other poultry may produce some problems because Guinea fowl will want to be in charge and will behave as if they are, shrieking and fighting at short notice.

3. *Must work on the market.*

Those who have kept Guineas have been surprised at the interest, but if to be kept commercially a real effort must be made to dispose of the birds as soon as they are ready.

Photo by]   [*Scholastic Photo Co.*

BLACK-CHESTED CRESTED GUINEA-FOWL (*Africa*).

In the crested Guinea-fowls the light speckling on the plumage is blue instead of white.

3
FEEDING
GUINEA FOWL

GENERAL PRINCIPLES

The feeding of Guinea fowl is rather like feed-ing normal poultry. They must have an adequate diet which is 'balanced' in the sense of giving the necessary nutrients for maintaining body weight and energy to produce eggs. The main require-ments are:

1. Water
2. Protein
3. Carbohydrates
4. Fats

Water

Without a regular and adequate supply of fresh water birds will very quickly become ill and un-productive. Accordingly, water fountains or a piped source are essential. If running free range a stream will be ideal, but not a stagnant pond or other place which might produce harmful bacte-ria, and thereby affect health.

Protein

Protein is the most expensive part of a diet and therefore getting it at the correct level is important. Corn and especially wheat is an excellent source of protein; around 11% is the usual figure. Peas, nuts, beans and soya are higher, but more expensive.

On the animal–food side the protein is quite high, but great care must be taken to ensure that all meats, fish and offal are cooked at a high temperature to remove any possible bacteria. As high as 60% may be obtainable and can be mixed with the other foods to get the desired balance.

Carbohydrates

These include the starches and sugars which produce the energy for body activity and maintenance. In a poultry ration carbohydrates are referred to as the 'fibre' and ideally should not be too high or there will be waste -- crude fibre is not digestible.

Fats

Fats in food supply the energy to maintain the body temperature. In fact, in poultry fat is stored up in the muscles, thus giving the bird its plumpness.

OTHER ESSENTIALS

Besides the obvious foods it will be essential to provide the following in some form:

1. Cod liver oil or its equivalent, especially for chicks for it avoids rickets and other, similar diseases.

2. Green foods and root vegetables. These act as a tonic and stimulate the digestive system. They are not high in food values, but are essential for sound health. Clover, chickweed, grass and other plants are included.

3. Charcoal.

This is not strictly a food, but is a necessary addition to the diet. It may be mixed with the food or kept in a separate container under cover. It helps to regulate the internal, digestive system.

4. Grit.

Grit is essential for calcium and for eggshells. It is found in oyster shells and similar items rich in carbonate of lime and which dissolve quickly.

There is also **flint grit** which is very small particles which do not readily dissolve (although they wear out). Ideally they should be sharp and very hard to act as "teeth" or "grinding" stones to help digest the food in the gizzard.

GRIT

In the wild, birds eat grit everyday even though they may lay only around thirty eggs per season. Obviously though, egg production is not the only consideration. Adequate nutrition requires an efficient digestive system and this depends upon the functioning of the gizzard. This will function without insoluble grit, but is much more effective when birds are able to eat as much grit as required.

Pheasants, doves, partridges, geese and other birds have been observed taking their daily intake of gravel or other grit. Percentages found in the crops of pheasants were 26 per cent and in Hungarian partridges it was 40 per cent. These were much higher than the grouse (6 per cent) and Mallard (13 per cent). They were not regarded as conclusive evidence of the normal intake percentages, but rather they confirm the need for regular supplies of grit.

SIZE OF GRIT

When grit is fed to birds it should be **appropriate to the size of the bird.** Birds such as grouse or pheasant should be supplied with small granules which they can consume easily in their gizzards should the supply be cut off. Smaller birds should be given grit which is rather like coarse sand. Poultry take pieces about 1mm square insoluble grit, but larger pieces may be picked up, especially flints used for grinding up food in the gizzard.

SELECTION OF FEEDING STUFFS

There are different approaches to feeding, influenced by the methods of management adopted. If on 'free range' a different system would apply than when producing intensively. More is covered on this matter in the chapters which deal with the different systems. The possibilities are as follows:

1. Wheat or Mixed Corn.

Provided wheat can be obtained from a farmer at a reasonable price this is the cheapest method and the easiest to administer. Unfortunately, corn merchants may charge more for corn than for compounded foods and this is bad news for the person who keeps livestock. In any event it is unwise to give wheat *only* because the correct balance is not being obtained. Wheat is low in protein so this deficiency must be made up.

It is useful as a food to scatter in litter or on grass so the birds can scratch for it. If on free range insects or worms and other foods will be found to counter-act the lack of balance.

2. Compounded Foods

The science of poultry feeding has reached a very high level and it is now known what vitamins, proteins, amino acids, trace elements and other essentials are needed for different purposes. The task has been taken over by the expert. Accordingly, it is simply a question of selecting the food for the stock involved. Thus:

(a) Chicks (keets)

These may be given chick crumbs or turkey starter crumbs which are recommended by many Guinea Fowl breeders because they help to develop the keets more quickly. Protein required is about 20%

(b) Growers

At about 4 weeks of age Growers' pellets can be introduced to give steady growth. Corn and layers' pellets may produce a more adequate mixture; sometimes Growers' seem to lack substance and by giving layers' these give the extra protein and calcium. Normal protein is about 15%.

(c) Layers' Pellets

These are specially formulated to give all the nutrients required for a laying hen. The protein content should be around 14 to 18 per cent.

External Food Hopper

Pellets or Mash?

The argument on the better type to use continues, but there is much in favour of using pellets, but not too big or the birds will have difficulty in swallowing them. The so-called 'mash' is
the food in powder form which is placed in hoppers and allows birds to feed constantly without
overfeeding. However, pellets are more palatable,
less wasteful and easier to handle, especially if
thrown on the ground. In wet weather they must
be place in a sheltered situation or the rain will
ruin them.

Mash used to be mixed with waste food such

Water Fountain
Give it a weekly clean

as old bread, but there is no advantage. Bread can be soaked in water, squeezed and then fed to the birds.

FEEDING INFLUENCED BY MANAGEMENT SYSTEM

The methods used for keeping Guinea fowl will influence the choice of food. Thus:

1. Small Flocks

Where they are kept free range, a feed of pellets in the morning and corn in the evenings will suffice. A free-standing automatic hopper may be used for the pellets but this should be kept indoors and the birds trained to use it, by keeping them inside for a few weeks when young.

2. Aviaries

As above for small flocks. However, green food should be given each day so the birds have a balanced diet.

3. Intensive – Barns, Deep Litter or Cages

Feed hoppers with automatic feeding and watering would be essential. Generally a small type of intensive pellet would be used which would be conveyed to the hoppers or troughs. Grit should also be provided in grit hoppers. Water would be provided in founts or by drinking nipples as in commercial poultry-keeping.

4
ANATOMY OF THE
GUINEA FOWL

PHYSICAL REQUIREMENTS

An understanding of how a bird functions is vital. It shows the physical requirements in terms of space and the food and other essentials to keep a fowl healthy. The digestive system and reproduction process are also worthy of study because, again, a poultry keeper must know what is feasible for him to maximise results.

A bird's anatomy may be viewed from two aspects:

1. The internal organs responsible for providing sustenance and the means of developing eggs in the female bird.

2. The outward form upon which a *standard* can be based.

An understanding of both is vital. The provision of appropriate food, water and minerals is vital to success. Unsuitable foods do not provide the essentials and can lead to health problems.

For the chicks higher protein foods develop bone, flesh and feathers and ensures rapid growth.

The outward shape, including the face, beak, crest, neck, body, legs, wings and feathers show the species of bird. As noted, it is on these features that a *standard* is based. The external shape and appearance also indicate important facts on the type of bird.

The structure of the Common Guinea Fowl is very similar to that of the domesticated fowl having identical features such as a breast bone and quite strong wings. Indeesd, because of its semi-domesticated state and the fact that it has not been 're-constituted' like most domesticated fowl the form varies very little from its appearance hundreds of years ago.

The main differences are to be found in the various colours or mutations now found with domesticated birds (discussed in Chapter 1.) and the special strains developed by the commercial farmers who produce birds for the table. The latter have been selected for their ability to convert food to flesh at a more economic rate, thus allowing them to be fattened quicker. They have also been kept in intensive conditions so that they are ready for the market quicker. Whether this trend will continue is debatable because free range management produces more natural tasting birds.

MAIN FEATURES OF THE GUINEA FOWL

The main parts of this very functional bird are now explained. The internal organs of a bird fit within a structure of bones, the skeleton. The principal parts are:--

1. Breastbone

The breastbone or sternum is a vital part of the body. It protects the internal organs as well as being a foundation for the flesh and muscles which operate the wings.

In describing a bird the *standard* usually denotes the depth of the body and qualifies this with such descriptions as "BODY: Back well filled". The Guinea fowl has a fairly upright carriage.

2. Wings

The wings provide the means of flying. Their positioning is of vital importance in determining *style* and *posture*: ; when carried high the thighs are revealed and the result is a taller looking bird. This is important for birds with "reach". With Guineas it is important to have strong wings which *are* used for flying.

3.   Legs and Feet

The legs and feet provide the means of walking, and perching.   They should be free from bumps or enlarged scales.

4.   Head

The head is mounted upon the neck which is quite flexible. At the front of the skull is the beak made up of the upper and lower mandibles. Size and shape of head is of vital importance. The helmet is a remarkable feature of this unusual species.

The Head of the Guinea Fowl

ANATOMY

The functioning of the bird is relatively simple and yet is an incredible process. Food is converted into flesh and/or eggs which, after incubation become chicks which rapidly grow into adult birds, and then at about 6-9 months of age they too become producers, thus repeating the process.
The main parts are as follows:

1.   Beak

Food is picked up by a bird and proceeds down the throat into the **crop**, a bag made of skin, and from there it goes on to the **gizzard**.

2.   Crop and Gizzard

The crop is the store for food just taken and this passes into a passageway known as a proventriculis (or ventriculus) before passing into the gizzard. The latter is an almost solid organ which masticates food so that it can be digested.

3.   Intestines

From the gizzard food passes into the intestines and after due processing, whereby the food is used in the blood stream, is passed out as faeces or 'droppings'.

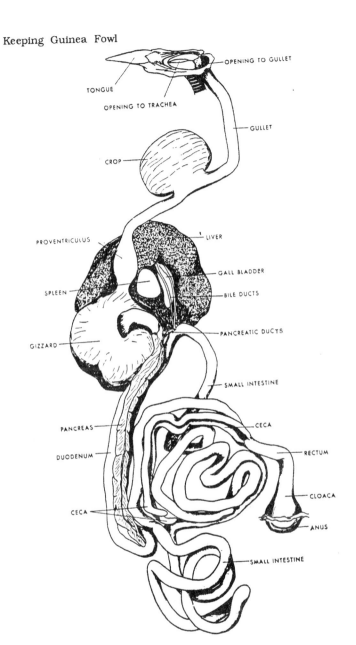

Digestive system of the Guinea Fowl

BLOOD AND AIR CIRCULATION

The blood is circulated by the contraction and expansion of the heart which is usually likened to a pump which has four chambers – the upper two named "auricles" and the lower two the "ventricles".

The bird breathes through its nostrils or mouth into the bronchial tubes and lungs. The arterial veins from the heart pass through the lungs thus allowing the circulating blood to be oxygenated.

REPRODUCTIVE SYSTEM

For successful reproduction both male and female should be in good health and well fed. Eggs should become fertile within a few days of male and female being placed together, but generally a period of ten days is considered to be a safe waiting time.

The female has two ovaries, only one of which usually develops. In addition, there is the oviduct: a long twisting tube consisting of two parts through which a yolk passes, adding the various parts ("white", membranes and shell) until the egg falls into the cloaca or egg pouch.

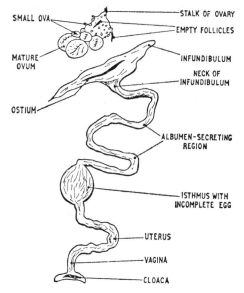

SMALL OVA
MATURE OVUM
OSTIUM

STALK OF OVARY
EMPTY FOLLICLES
INFUNDIBULUM
NECK OF INFUNDIBULUM
ALBUMEN-SECRETING REGION
ISTHMUS WITH INCOMPLETE EGG
UTERUS
VAGINA
CLOACA

Female

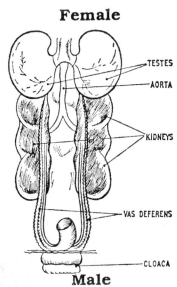

TESTES
AORTA
KIDNEYS
VAS DEFERENS
CLOACA

Male

The Reproductive Systems

Opinions on how long the process takes vary,but generally around eighteen hours is regarded as the cycle time. Within the ovary of a fowl there may be hundreds of embryo eggs (oocytes). The Guinea fowl is not as prolific so the number would be smaller, but the principle is still the same. These oocytes develop so that a few large yolks ripen (usually about five) until one is ready to go into the oviduct for development into the egg.

The male bird "treads" the hen and thereby fertilises the eggs. He discharges semen from testes into two ducts and thence into the oviduct of the female when the mating takes place. In this way the egg becomes fertile and after a period of 26 to 28 days the embryo is a fully developed chick, known as a keet and pecks its way out of the egg.

KEET

5

THE EGG

NECESSARY ATTRIBUTES

There are many factors exhibited by an egg which should be recognised for successful incubation and for commercial exploitation of the eggs produced for sale.

Factors which tend to be of importance are as follows:

1. **Size**
2. **Shape**
3. **Colour**
4. **Bloom** (the cuticle which should have a glossy finish)

Guinea fowl eggs excel in quality with thick shells which protect the contents. The size is around 1.5 oz. compared with the fowl's egg of 2.0 oz. or more.

SIZE

Size of the egg is important, but very little has been done to develop the Guinea fowl egg further because the effort would not be worthwhile, although efforts have been made to produce hybrid birds for the table, with considerable success. In fact, the eggs tend to be more valuable for hatching than for eating.

This is not to suggest the egg is undesirable for culinary purposes. Its yolk may be larger than the fowl's egg and this is dark and rich with a pleasing flavour. In fact, it is for the person who likes a well flavoured egg without any of the 'strongness' of the duck egg.

A comparison with the weights of eggs of other domesticated birds is as follows:

Comparison in Grammes
(approx.)

1.	Domestic fowl	58 – 68
2.	Domestic duck	80
3.	Domestic turkey	85
4.	Guinea fowl	40 – 58
5.	Bantams	38 – 38
6.	Geese (domestic)	200
7.	Pheasant	32
8.	Peafowl	90

All the weights are approximate and are given as a guide to the relative sizes. When incubating the size is of great importance and generally speaking mixing widely differing sizes together is not recommended.

SHAPE

The shape of the egg is brought about by the muscles in the oviduct. A smaller egg than normal passing through an oviduct will tend to be spherical.

Heredity factors determine the shape and, therefore, the correct selection of the eggs for incubation should produce layers which will produce similar shaped eggs, provided the cock used is from a strain which also lays similar shaped eggs. The introduction of a new strain may upset the shape – a round egg strain will be changed with new blood which was bred from conical shaped eggs.

Variations in shape within reasonable limits do not affect hatchability. Obviously, though, abnormal shapes will not usually hatch, nor is it desirable they should. Small eggs with little or no yolk come into this category. The double-yolked egg arises from the simultaneous growth of the ova which are then released together.

Both size and shape are affected by the presence of double yolks.   Theoretically there is no reason why double-yolked eggs should not hatch, but the experience of the author has been that they are not fertile.   Obviously they are best excluded from a setting.

Cleanliness is Vital

Note: Whilst the exterior of the egg is important it will be essential to ensure that the eggs produced are free from blood spots or other foreign bodies. These may be revealed from inspection by candling.

Obviously, in the interests of better results the sheds should be cleaned regularly and shavings or other litter spread to 2-3 inches thick and then added to until it is quite thick (deep litter system) or cleaned out each week and the litter replenished.

Dirt from mud or from accumulated dirt in the nest box should also be removed. Nest boxes should also be cleaned and fresh straw or shavings added, thus avoiding the accumulation of dirt which will encourage parasites. If mud is carried in from the run then place gravel near the entrance which can be washed down at regular intervals, thus keeping dirt outside.

A droppings board with perches above will also help to keep a shed free from droppings on the floor and is easier to clean.

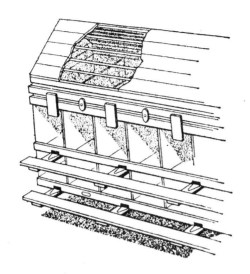

Nest Boxes
Note the platform at the front for easy access

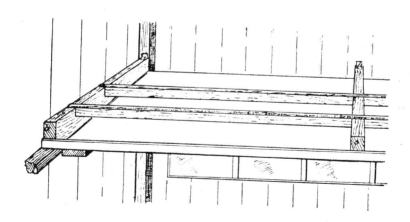

Droppings Board
**Should be removable for easy cleaning; perches are in slots
for removal**

EGG COLOUR

The colour of the egg is one of the mysteries of nature. It is only in recent years that ornitholigists have discovered the source of the colour.

Egg Colour

The actual colour comes from glands in the oviduct and is transferred by pigments:

(a) oocyanin – Basal Blue

(b) ooclilomin – Yellow

(c) ooxanthin – Red or Purplish

(d) ooporphrin – pattern forming

· This colouring stage takes place in the lower part of the oviduct known as the uterus and it is at this point that a coating of calcium carbonate is coated over the shell membrane.

The Guinea Fowl Egg

In the case of Guinea fowl the eggs are a sandy or brown colour, sometimes with spots, looking very much like the egg of a wild bird. Because the shells are thicker than the normal egg, plus the dark colour, it can be a problem to 'candle'; ie, to test whether the embryo is developing. Ultra-violet light may be employed to assist in the candling process.

THE EGG

Note: Terms are self explanatory except the CHALAZAE which is a special part of the albumen

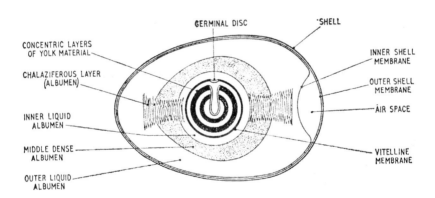

Parts of the Egg

BLOOM
Creating the Shell

The top–quality shell comes from the healthy bird, managed in a suitable environment with the appropriate type of food, water and other essentials.

Birds flying out of doors with access to grass, vegetation, earth and other natural objects usually produce eggs of good quality. The calcium carbonate required to produce the shell comes from the food eaten and from sand, stones, leaves and other small items picked up. Limestone is the main ingredient for the shell substance and yet nowhere will it be obviously available.

Proper functioning requires the quantity absorbed to be considered and must be consumed by each hen according to her requirements. Birds kept in cages or aviaries, may be given fine oyster shell and limestone provided in suitable hoppers. If topped up regularly the hens will regulate their own consumption.

Grit Hopper

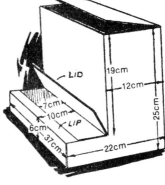

The Shell – General Notes

The outer shell of the egg is made up of three distinct layers:

1. **Cuticle** – a fine coating which gives the egg its lustre or bloom.

2. **Palisade** or spongy Layer – the bulk of the shell (approx 2/3 of the thickness).

3. **Mammillary** – the inner part

The shell is very strong and relative to its size can withstand great pressure (Hen egg: 60 gramme, 4.1 kilos breaking strength, whereas a small fresh egg, 1 gramme in weight, will withstand 0.1 kilo – the Canary egg is around 2 grammes in weight). Guinea fowl 40 grammes in weight has a breaking strength of about 5.0 kilos.

6

BREEDING

THE BREEDING PEN

A hen and a cock may be run together as a breeding pair*. A trio-- **two hens to a cock--** may also be quite successful; in fact, up to 6 hens to a cock could be successful, provided they are kept in an aviary when the breeding flock is running together in reasonably close confinement. Those with free range will find that the cock will run with many hens, but fertility may vary. Generally, it is unwise to have more than one male bird in an *enclosed* breeding pen because there will be scuffles and fights.

A youngish cockerel is to be preferred with hens of one or two years old. The more mature hens tend to produce stronger chicks**. Laying starts in March and April and continues into the late Summer or even Autumn. Generally a clutch of eggs will be laid, say, 25/30 and then the Guinea hen will come broody and, if running outdoors,

* Some naturalists have suggested that 1 to 1 is the natural order, GF being mated to one partner for life, but a mixed flock is the usual state in domestication. ** Chicks are known as Keets (keats).

she will sit on the eggs.

Even if kept indoors for roosting -- desirable because of foxes-- the hens may still lay in a quiet place such as under a bush, in an old tree hollow or in grass or undergrowth. If so, the eggs should be collected and taken to the place where eggs are stored.   In their place it is wise to place old eggs (marked) or pot eggs. When collecting the eggs never disturb the hen or she may desert the nest. This is undesirable because finding nests may be difficult enough and will involve watching the hen, or possibly the cock, who might give away the hiding place by lurking around the spot. Nevertheless, it can be very difficult so always be ready for a proud mother to appear with around 10 chicks.

Once the chicks are fairly independent she will start laying again and repeat the process. Unfortunately, because Guineas are quite wild, if left to roam, she will run the chicks to the point of exhaustion, and if the weather is wet, they will become chilled and die.

It is better therefore to catch her up by driving her into a pen -- scatter food and leave the door open and entice her in. Do not try to run her in, or the chicks will scatter, just like wild Game birds, and they will be lost. The young chicks may run into a corner or other hiding place and if not found will become chilled and die.

Achieving Breeding Condition

Ample food in the form of layer's pellets and greenstuff will bring birds into condition quickly, especially if only mixed corn has been fed during the winter months. With the longer, lighter Spring days the hens will start to look 'brighter' and will start to lay. This is the time to start making arrangements to breed.

Letting Guineas run outside is the best way of getting the birds into condition. They will eat the insects which come with Spring. Scratching around they will find all sorts of titbits as well as choice young greenstuff and grit; all will help to encourage breeding.

If kept in an aviary or pen there may be a need for a higher protein diet. Some breeders advocate using Breeders' pellets which will have approaching 20% protein. Remember though that an excessive protein diet may not benefit the birds and will be costly. We have found that birds given the small size Layers' pellets and adequate greenstuff will perform quite well.

Water should be changed on a regular basis and a careful watch kept on the overall condition. Mopey cocks or hens will not breed, or, if they will, should not be tolerated, because their progeny will tend to inherit the problems of the parents.

Egg Collection

Eggs should be collected and stored in a box containing clean sawdust, marked with the date and a code for the pen and then saved until enough eggs are available for incubating.

Stale eggs will not hatch; those saved should be turned each day -- mark with a pencil cross on one side and turn to allow the cross to show on alternate days. Also mark the eggs with a code for the date. Some poultry keepers advocate leaving a pot egg in place of the egg removed , but it will be appreciated that leaving dummy eggs does tend to encourage broodiness.

If kept in an aviary two or more hens may lay in the same nest box. The standard type of nest box for poultry can be provided. Try to collect eggs at a regular time and minimize the disturbance of the hens on the nest. Guinea hens are very wild so what appears to be an attack on the nest will not be welcome.

A special storage box or Keyes trays may be used for storing larger quantities of eggs and, where necessary, when incubating artificially, the eggs may be washed in a special solution which prevents contamination. In addition, for large scale production, an egg store, maintained at a level of

50 to 60 degrees F. Eggs should not be kept for longer than 10 days. If a satisfactory " per cent hatchability" is to be obtained very strict rules must be observed on the matters mentioned, viz:

1. **Healthy stock.**
2. **Satisfactory feeding.**
3. **Correct combination of hens to virile cock.**
4. **Daily collection of eggs and correct storage at a temperature which is not too high.**
5. **"Disinfect" the eggs in a special way with a solution developed for that purpose by a veterinary medicine manufacturer.**
The need for the sterilization applies to artificial incubation. Under normal circumstances, unless eggs are seen to be dirty, those under a broody hen do not seem to suffer from infection problems; the hen, when sitting, coats the shell with a protective coating which resists penetration. This is a subject which can be observed when checking eggs, but does not appear to have been developed by commercial breeders.
6. **Follow the normal procedures for broody hen or incubator and ensure that ideal hatching conditions are achieved.**

Care and attention to the daily tasks should ensure that the eggs are fertile. With good management around 80% hatchability can be achieved, but this has to be worked for or results may be less than 50% which is unacceptable.

Method of Approach

The incubation of the eggs may be accomplished by one of the following methods:

1. Guinea fowl Hen

Using the hen to hatch her own eggs is natural, but this will not maximize egg production. In addition, the hen may be wild and nervous with the result that chicks may be lost. In ideal conditions, with eggs being collected daily, a hen may lay 80 t0 100 eggs, but if allowed to go broody, she may lay half the quantity.

2. Bantam, Silkie or other Broody

Provided a steady, small-sized hen is selected this will probably give the best results. Around 10-12 eggs should be adequate. A broody nest would be formed, using a large turf to form the cavity. Make sure the hen covers the eggs and they are not rolling out from under her by making a basin-like nest, with earth bottom and lined with straw.

3. Small Incubator

A small **still-air incubator** will be adequate for the amateur or smallholder. These take from 50 eggs upwards and some are even smaller. Turn the eggs **at least** twice daily and candle the eggs at 7 days and 14days. This involves using a spotlight which lights up the contents of the egg to show whether the embryo is present and growing. If eggs are clear, which may occur early in the season, then the fertility of the

cock may be in doubt. Try changing for a **cockerel**
until the weather is warmer and then go back to the
older bird. A guide to the various stages may be seen
from the drawing given.

4. Forced Draught Incubator

This is the incubator for the large scale producer who
wishes to have the eggs turned automatically and the
ventilation controlled to a degree. Tight controls for
humidity are also critical because of the thickness of
the shell.

Hatching Temperature

The temperature recommended is 103
degrees F (36 C) or slightly less for 26 to 28 days.
Overheating must be avoided. Much depends on
the incubator and the manufacture's instructions
must be followed. Humidity for Guinea eggs is approaching 60% and this should be the aim (generally speaking the ideal humidity for any incubation
is 50 to 60%) .

A Typical Small Incubator
**Many types exist, some with automatic turning and electronic
temperature control.**

7thDay

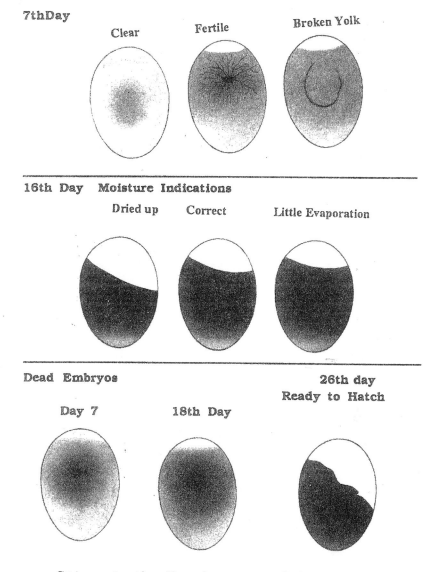

Clear   Fertile   Broken Yolk

16th Day   Moisture Indications

Dried up   Correct   Little Evaporation

Dead Embryos

**26th day
Ready to Hatch**

Day 7   18th Day

Stages in the Development of the Embryo.

This is useful as a guide for candling. It is only an approximate guide because the air space may diminish at varying rates depending on humidity.

The Eggs

As noted, eggs take 28 days to hatch, but between 26 and 28 days is usual with 27 days the norm. The average size is 4.9cm x 3.7cm, which is around the same size as the Jungle Fowl. The weight is 40 grammes, again like the Jungle Fowl, and a domestic fowl is around 70g.

Period		Weight gain (g)	Food consumption (g) (x)	Conversion index (x)
0–4	weeks	380	670	1,76
5–8	weeks	590	1690	2,86
9–11	weeks	400	1735	4,34
12	weeks	110	630	5,73
13	weeks	100	635	6,35
0–11	weeks	1370	4095	2,99
0–12	weeks	1480	4725	3,19
0–13	weeks	1580	5360	3,39

x. Ration assayed at M.E. 3000 k.cal / kg.
   Ambient temperature 20°C.
g. grammes

Keets Food Conversion Table at different ages
See text p 58

REARING THE KEETS

Rearing the keets can present problems, especially for the first week. A few simple rules may
be helpful:

1. Keep Dry and Warm

Generally keets should be kept indoors for at least a few weeks and then
under cover even when being reared after
they are feathered.

If a brooder is to be used start at
around 90° F and reduce the heat gradu-
ally by 5 degrees each week. Observe the
keets to ensure they are neither too hot (
gasping for breath) or too cold (huddled
together).

Ensure that there is an outer exercise
area for them to emerge from the brooder,
so they harden off as quickly as possible.
An infra-red light suspended from the
ceiling will also suffice provided there is a
canopy over the light which can be raised
as the chicks grow.

2. Supply with Adequate Food and Water

After the first few days feed the chicks
outside the brooder. Ensure the water is
changed daily.

3. If a broody hen is used make sure she can look after the keets without trampling on them.

A special coop and run may be used or the hen and keets may be in an enclosed run where than be at full liberty with the surrogate mother. With a large hen such as a Rhode Island Red as many as 25 keets may be feasible and if a number of eggs are set at the same time the hatchings may be grouped together. However, after a few days do not try to introduce new chicks for there is a danger they will be killed.

Floor litter should consist of wood shavings or leaves, but limit the depth in the early stages or chicks may get buried as the hen scratches. The chick fount should be checked each day to ensure that litter does not block the drinking area for this will foul the water and lead to the spreading of disease. Changing water each day is vital.

Feeding

Turkey starter or chick crumbs should be fed for 2-3 weeks with no other food except a daily bunch of chickweed or other acceptable greenstuff. Do not feed long, coarse grass which can lead to impact crop problems. (cont. p 58)

A Typical Brooder

An Infra-red Lamp

After that introduce broken corn and, at 5 weeks, feed growers' pellets. Watch the development of the chicks and, if not progressing, introduce an occasional feed of high protein food such as Broiler pellets which act as a tonic and stimulate growth.

If rearing for the table a high protein diet is advisable. Thus the start can be 24% protein which is dropped to 18% at 5 weeks and 14% at 9 weeks. The food conversion rate may be seen from the Table shown (Courtesy: *Practical Poultry-keeping*, Batty, J).

Those being reared for future breeding can be allowed to mature more slowly so they develop at the normal rate to maturity.

Killing Table Birds

Generally the keets will be ready for marketing at around 14 weeks with a possible range of 12 to 16 weeks depending upon syestem and progress being made. Weights should be about 0.50 kilos (1.1lb.) and up to 1kilo or just over. The conversion ratio at 16 weeks may be as high as 5:1. Killing is no problem and may be done by hand by neck dislocation.

Plucking is also straight forward, but for a commercial market it will be essential to acquire:

1. **Plucking machine:** dry or wet (latter preferred).

2. **Refrigerator** to keep birds fresh and a freezer if birds are to be sold in a frozen state.

3. **Packing facilities** for packing in plastic backs with a 'brand name' to attract the consumer. It is also advisable to indicate the merits of Guinea as a table bird.

Typical Free range Layout
A number of medium size Sheds avoids the 'burnt' grass effect

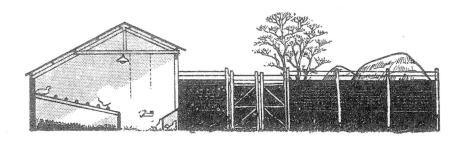

The Barn System
Guineas must have adequate ventilation so , along with the Pole Barn system, this method is ideal.

7

BASIC SYSTEMS

POSSIBLE APPROACHES

There are many systems available for keeping poultry including Guinea Fowl:

1. Free Range

"Free Range" means the birds have full and free access to the outside, leaving and returning as they think fit. It is the **Natural** method which has many advantages and is regarded by many as being more humane than the other methods.

There are also disadvantages including the cost of land and possible loss of production in inclement weather.

A modified practical definition is considered later in this chapter.

2. Restricted Free Range

Birds may be kept in feed units on grass or in pens, but with less land than **full** free range. For those with limited space this is possibly the best compromise, but has its limitations especially on the numbers which may be kept.

3. Semi-Intensive (including straw yard , barn and aviary systems)

The semi-intensive system means that the birds have access to a grass run, but may be kept indoors when the weather is inclement.   In addtion, the amount of space available in the outside run is less than free range.

A modification is the farm-yard or straw-yard system, whereby poultry are allowed to roam around an enclosed yard which is littered with straw.

4. Battery Cages

Although still used the battery cage system has run into difficulties, especially in relation to health and hygiene and is being modified to allow more birds per cage and better facilities. Guinea fowl may not be ideal inmates for cages; a docile strain would have to be developed.

THE CHOICE

All the systems 1 to 3 inclusive enable birds to enjoy considerable freedom, to scratch and pick up green stuff, grit, grubs and other essentials.   Above all, Guinea Fowl must be kept interested so that they are constantly engaged finding food and enjoying it.   Happy birds are productive birds.

The main features of these methods are now considered.

A
Lean-to
Intensive
House.

A "Span
Roof"
House
with
"Top
Lights."

CANVAS

A Movable House . A Backgarden
House.

A
Tolman Long Slope House

A Sussex
"Ark."

A Variety of small Houses

These may be used on free range or with runs attached as semi-intensive.

SIZE OF HOLDING?

A fundamental problem with free range is how big is the operation to reach. If relatively small with ,say, 100 birds, then the problems are not usually serious. Once the intention is to keep 1000 birds **and upwards** the difficulties multiply.

For the **small to medium size** type of operation with one or two fields available the free-range poultry keeping should be able to avoid all the excesses likely to cause problems. These are as follows:

1.   **Overcrowding**
2.   **Sour ground**
3   **Disease becoming established in the ground so that each generation of birds has a high rate of mortality or poor production**
4.   **Disturbances due to behaviour of birds; fighting, overlapping of territories and the inevitable establishment of the "pecking order".**

OVERCROWDING

Signs of overcrowding will be reflected in the ground becoming sour and the grass disappearing - usually in large patches, around and near the poultry houses. Once denuded there is great difficulty in getting the grass to grow at all. Instead of having natural surroundings to keep them occupied the birds are left to mope around or to stray further and further away with the inherent dangers of being killed by dogs, foxes or traffic.

Sites which are very exposed – a large open field – will tend to suffer from denuding of the grass, especially in summer. Some form of sprinkler system will overcome the problem, provided the density of stocking is reasonable. With too many birds per acre nothing can stop the effects of wear and tear on the land.

Accordingly, a shaded spot is better with the sheds and large patches of the grass area being out of the direct rays of the sun. It is for this reason that many orchards have been used for keeping free range birds.

Exercise & Food

They can scratch under the fruit trees and will clear the area of insect pests. In addition, they will keep the grass short and eat any apples or pears which fall from the trees. Obviously though there is a limit to the number of birds which can be kept and the trees may make access to poultry houses quite difficult. For a small number of birds the system is ideal.

Avoiding Stress

Overcrowding leads to stress in poultry. If too many are together or in small houses, but in near proximity, bullying and feather pecking will result with a loss in productivity. Moreover, the poor producers may not be detected with a lowering of the average per flock.

SOUR GROUND

The poultry farmer is faced with a dilemma. He must run birds on the land to the maximum possible extent, thus making the most of his investment and manuring the land to the full, yet he has to observe strict rules of good stock management and hygiene or within two or three years he will suffer quite serious problems.

Steps to be taken to avoid the effects of over intensive stocking are:

**1. Move the sheds and the flocks to new
ground each year.** This is the safest way. However, it does represent a great deal of trouble. A
more easily managed system would be to have
duplicate housing and after two years to sell off
the stock leaving the sheds available for a year for
disinfecting, creosoting, etc. and then to restock.

Sheds with wheels or on skids can help if
moves are to be made with the poultry houses.

**2. Pay special attention to removal of
manure and to installing methods of keeping
faeces separate so the hens do not have to
tread in it.**

3. Inspect stock regularly and pick them up
to check if they are producing.

4. Cull any wasters -- those with obvious
disabilities which do not lay. Runny eyes, ruffled
feathers, moping and lack of energy.

INTENSIVE SYSTEM

The intensive system means keeping a large number of birds in a limited space. It may be distinguished by reference to the system of management:

(a) Regular cleaning and replacement of litter; e.g. shavings, peat moss.

(b) **Deep litter** when a very thick layer of shavings is put into the shed and kept for 6 months or longer without being cleaned out.

(c) **Battery system** which entails keeping birds in cages and having food and water provided quite automatically. **Cages are provided** to house a number of birds within an enclosed environment.

SPECIFICATIONS OF CAGES

The cages should comply with specified standards laid down by the regulations of the country concerned e.g. EEC regulations would apply to the countries in the Community. Birds confined in too small a space, or too many birds per cage can result in lost production as well as unhealthy hens. Bones become brittle, feathers are worn and birds become pale and lacking vitality.

Essentials are as follows:

1. Reasonable capital cost per bird
2. Large enough for birds to turn around
3. Bars designed so as to give maximum access to

food and water for all occupants and yet not catch or rub
feathers.

4.   A monitoring system to be able to watch over
birds on a regular basis

SELECTION OF APPROPRIATE SYSTEM

The above systems may be adopted in their
entirety or in some form of combination e.g. free
range for most times, but semi–intensive during
the winter.   Practical considerations are as follows:

1.   Public Opinion

In recent years there has been a wave of feel-
ing which is in opposition to intensive systems or
any methods which appear to restrain birds or
over–crowds them.   Free range eggs or 'natural'
table birds may be sold at a higher price which
helps to offset the increased costs.

2.   Capital Costs

A fully intensive house must be properly insulated   and   have   special   ventilation   (usually
fans).   In addition, the cages, plumbing, automatic   feeding   system,   controlled   lighting   and
other requirements all add to the very high capital costs.

Free range systems are cheaper to install,
but the labour costs of feeding and management
are higher.

3.   Land Availability

Free range requires considerable land and,
therefore, when large numbers of birds are to be
kept a farm is essential.

What is Meant by "Free Range" ?

Opinions differ on the space required for the pure system of free-range poultry management. It seems certain that *not more* than 100 birds per acre should be kept. The semi-intensive system may allow 300 birds per acre or, with clever management, even more. However, it will be appreciated that any attempt at overcrowding could lead to severe problems (discussed later).

4.   Type of Land

Land which becomes waterlogged and muddy is not ideal for poultry farming. On the other hand, dry, sandy scrub-land will not supply luscious green grass. The latter is excellent food for birds and, in effect, is free. Accordingly, its use would be maximised.

Very hot open areas are not conducive to maximum results. Trees or hedgerows may provide some shade. The siting of the houses will also affect the exposure to the weather.

Some breeds are more suitable than others for heavy soils and these should be selected with care .

5.   Access to Services

Poultry require a regular flow of clean, pure water. Accordingly, some form of piped system is essential. Hose pipes can be used but there is a limit to the size of range which can be watered. The problems of freezing–up can also be serious.

The foodstuffs, grit, etc. can be transported by tractor and trailer or on a four wheel vehicle.

Lighting is vital and power is desirable so again provision of this service should be considered. The effect of lighting on the perrformance of Guinea fowl has not been explored to the full, but if kept intensively it will be necessary to provide around 12 hours of light.

The ventilation provision must also be covered with fans or similar means. It is acknowledged that from 10 – 12 weeks this aspect should receive special attention.

A Broiler–type house is probably the most practical, but perches should also be provided because Guinea fowl prefer to roost rather than crouch.

Practical Considerations

Bearing the above factors in mind it is useful to summarise some of the matters to be examined:

1. Domestic Housing

Adequate housing for the poultry farmer and his family will be essential. Adjacent to the house should be outbuildings for the following:

(a)   **food storage and mixing room;**

(b)   **egg storage;**

(c)   **gate-sales shop;**

(d)   **incubation room (if required)**

2. Access to Range

Full access to the range is a vital requrement. Hilly, undulating terrain should be avoided not only because of the difficulties of reaching the poultry houses, but also the inherent problems of security from foxes and thieves.

3.   Ease of Partitioning for Field Rotation

For many reasons, including the control of diseases, it is desirable to rest each area to allow the grass to grow and to avoid infestation with disease carrying bacterias. Careful planning will repay itself many times over.

4.   Privacy for Birds

Birds should be kept free from disturbance. Guinea fowl are very excitable so should not be subjected to sudden noises or attacks from dogs or other predators.

A MODIFIED DEFINITION OF FREE RANGE

Free access to a large area such as a field is the recognised definition of "free range". A population density of 50 to 100 birds per acre gives a guide to what is required. Assuming 100 birds per acre and allowing for a rotation system with changes every 6 months, 20 acres will be required per 1000 birds.

*For obvious reasons the **pure form** of free range may not be very profitable.*

Instead, a *modified* type of free range may be necessary. Essentially the requirement is access to fresh air and a plentiful supply of natural foods without the fouling of the grounds. A great deal can be done to provide the necessary **ingredients** of free range.

The fresh air is no problem so the remainder must be provided in a variety of ways; for example:

1. **Access to grass** with a regular change over of birds to fresh pasture, thus allowing the grass to grow again.

2. **The fold system,** moving the arks across the field on a regular basis.

3. **Pens/aviaries/barns** in which supplements are regularly given by the addition of grass clippings, weeds, leaves and other foundation material.

4. **Watch out for watery eyes , runny droppings, ruffled feathers, fish eyes and other signs of being out of condition.** Handling and carrying out simple tests can eliminate the wasters.

5. **Test eggs and meat of birds at regular intervals to make sure quality is maintained.**

6. **Watch for bullying and any malpractices such as egg eating.**

FREE RANGE PROBLEMS

Psychologically free range poultry keeping will always appear better than any other system. Fresh air, open spaces, natural food and freedom should lead to healthier birds and, therefore, better eggs or meat. No matter what scientists or poultry farmers state, the idea that **natural is best** will always prevail.

In an attempt to show there can be serious disadvantages it is necessary to consider some of the main problems which are as follows:

1.Productivity

Because of the climatic differences and the advent of the moult around 70 per cent production is in the Spring/Summer period and the remaining 30 per cent in the Autumn/Winter period.

2. Health of Birds

In modern times discoveries have been made which show that hens kept in cages develop brittle bones which may break easily. There is also a serious problem from disease, particularly salmonella, which has affected the acceptability of eggs as food.

Complacency, lack of controls, keeping very large flocks, absence of fresh air and many other factors have been blamed. Fortunately, the danger has been found and the alarm raised. Steps have been taken to avoid outbreaks of disease, where appropriate to give larger cages and alternative systems to allow each hen more space.

What should also be remembered is that free range can also be subject to disease, which may wipe out complete flocks. Therefore, hygiene and being run on "clean" ground is essential. Food fed to birds is excreted all around and comes with it potential disease, including coccidiosis and worms.

Each bird will excrete around 200 lb. of fresh droppings each year so imagine the output from 1000 birds on a field. This manure contains about 1.5 per cent nitrogen and essentially will make the grass grow rich and green. Accordingly, if birds are transferred every six months and the ground allowed to "rest", possibly being limed, then the manure can do much good. However, if birds are kept on for long periods without rotation, the ground becomes sour and disease carrying, with the resultant deterioration in the health of the hens.

FULL FREE RANGE REQUIREMENTS

As noted earlier, for full range to apply it is essential to have a field on which suitable poultry houses are sited. The hens are let out each day and closed up each evening. They thus have access to a maximum amount of grass which is a valuable source of food and which enriches the colour of the yolk to a deep yellow.

Security

The poultry houses are usually sited near the dwelling house so the farmer can keep the brds under observation. Opinions differ on how much fencing is necesary. Possibilities are:

1. **No special fencing,** but place the poultry houses well away from public roads so that birds do not stray and get killed or stolen.

2. **Wire netting partitions** which allow each flock to be kept separate. Hedges are useful for providing shade.

8

HOUSING

HOUSING SIZES

The houses for free range have to be of the type which will give adequate space for normal occupation and possibly an extra area for **scratching** when the weather is very inclement.

A rule of thumb is that each bird should be allowed 10 cubic ft for roosting purposes; however it is never as simple as that. Design and positioning of perches, doors, pop holes, nest boxes and food containers all affect the space required.

In the evening, when the birds have gone to roost, look at them in situation and see how much perching space is left. If they are overcrowded with some birds not perching, then it is likely that the design is faulty or the house is too small.

As noted, Guinea fowl prefer to perch so a full range would be provided, thus allowing a bird to establish his own area for roosting.

An example of the calculation involved is as follows:

1. *Roosting Space by area*:: L x W x H = No of fowl

Example 6 x 4 x 5ft = 120 = 12 birds

This is for the conventional poultry shed.

2. *Roosting Space by Perch Space*
Example **as above** with perches length ways 18 birds can be kept. Allow **three** perches with a 2ft space at the front for flying up and down. Perches should be in steps.

This is for the open–fronted shed.

3. *Intensive Houses* : allow 4–5 sq ft of floor space per hen.
This measure is important because it must allow enough scratching space per bird. A house 6x 4ft will house 5 or 6 adult birds.

With **Barn** or **Aviary** systems the "shelves", mezzanine floors and other means of increasing floor space allow more birds to be kept, but this must be used with caution or overcrowding will result.

Intensive Housing for Game Birds
**Guinea fowl, pheasants and quail have been successful in
this Maywick Gas heated, automatic system.**
Courtesy: Jay Publicity Ltd -- Jim Sargant

RUNS

Runs are an essential part of poultry keeping.They supply fresh air, exercise and general interest which cuts out boredom.

Green food, leaves and other additions ensure they are kept active and eager to forage around. A guide on space is :

1. Grass land such as fields , paddocks and orchards.

Allow 100 sq. ft for each bird. A plot of 50 x 50 ft would take 25 hens. Opinions differ on the optimum number , but around 50 maximum per flock is advisable.

2. Gardens

Allow about 20 sq. ft per bird as well as the allowance for the shed.

3. Intensive Free Range

As many as 400 birds to the acre may be possible for relatively short periods, but movement to a different site will be essential every 6 months or so depending upon conditions. Half this number is possible on ploughed land.

If on a permanent basis not more than 100 per acre is advisable.

These measurements are a guide only. The type of soil , time of year , weather conditions and other factors affect the stock intensity.

In winter to keep birds in lay or growing it may be advisable to keep birds indoors , thus conserving heat . A scratching shed with peat moss , leaves , shavings or other litter is essential or, of course, kept in an intensive house.

80

Semi-intensive System for Guinea Fowl
(Courtesy: *Poultry World*)

Housing breaks down into the form of building used, for example:

1.   Poultry sheds of varying sizes to cater for the size of flocks being kept.

There is conflict between the size required for centralised control with large houses holding, say, 3,000 birds and the small unit for 100 layers. The latter gives a more realistic grazing area, but is rather costly when it comes to providing food and services. For large scale operations the large house will be essential because automation will be vital. A stockholding of 10,000, allowing for rest periods for the grass, should have a 100 acre farm, but in practice this size of flock may be housed on, say, 30 acres which in the long run will lead to overcrowding.

2.   Fold units which give free access to grass and yet do not require fences.

3.   Special Houses, usually for the larger poultry farmer, e.g.
    (a)   slatted floor levels;
    (b)   polyproplene/plastic/fibre glass units. These new materials offer tremendous scope, but have not been tried fully.

SMALL SHEDS

These come in various shapes and sizes. Generally, units should be reasonably small to avoid large numbers in one shed so that bullying and other problems are avoided. The stocking rate recommended is generally **three birds** per square metre.

Every part of the shed should be used and, therefore, provision should be made to have nest boxes about floor level and food troughs in positions which enable food to be reached, but without food being contaminated from litter or droppings.

Similarly, water should be provided in water fountains in each shed or outside. The advantage of the latter is that there is less danger of water running low because the founts can be checked each day.

The Sussex Ark
This is suitable for keeping a few birds but is rather restricting for adult
Guinea Fowl.

THE SUSSEX ARK

One of the best known poultry sheds for the small scale commercial operation is the Sussex Ark, said to have been named because its shape resembles the biblical ark. Its main features are :

1. **Low, being no more than 5 ft at the eaves , thus being economic to build.**
2. **Two doors --one in the top and the other at the front.**
3.**Slatted floor so that droppings fall through into cavity.**
4. **Slatted floor can be removed for ease of cleaning.**
5. **Ventilation is at the eaves but also through the floor area.**
6. **Construction is by means of overlapping boards.**

The unique natural ventilation enables birds to thrive and remain very healthy and can be employed in a colony system without difficulties once the birds have become accustomed to their own ark. For layers it will be necessary to put a three-compartment nest box for up to 15 layers.

PENS AND ENCLOSURES

In suitable conditions the stock is let out into a field each day. Ideally a flock should have a plentiful supply of fresh grass.

Because of predators, birds must be locked away each evening. There is also the need to train them to become accustomed to a particular house so that they will return to it to roost each evening. **Suitable perches and dropping boards must be provided.**

An alternative to the **open-field approach** is to have separate pens to accommodate, say, 50 birds. Wire netting partitions or other barriers are used with a gate for access. If breeding is to be allowed, with cockerels running in the pens, it will be necessary to board up the lower part of the fence so that squabbles between the males will be avoided.

SOIL SUITABILITY AND 'BURNT GRASS' EF-FECT

For free range to be successful, attention must be paid to the type and condition of the soil. A well drained, light loam is ideal so that mud is kept to a minimum; if necessary small pebbles or gravel can be placed near popholes and the door so that mud is not carried indoors and possibly onto the eggs.

The **Burnt Grass effect** can be avoided by putting birds on fresh land at regular intervals with sufficient time to allow new grass to grow. There is a conflict; **low** stocking will save wear on grass, but will not provide adequate use of the land, building and equipment.

NOTE: there is always a tendency for birds to stay within easy reach of the house where food and water are available. Thus with the large house the existing grass near the house will quickly disappear and the question is what next? Movement of the stock is the ideal, but cannot always be done very easily. The provision of grass clippings from lawns, paddocks, etc., may provide a solution and the dumping of leaves and similar foraging material is desirable, provided always that the litter is edible and no danger to health.

The Rotomaid system for washing eggs
**Eggs must be clean and for setting should be sterilized with a
special solution available for this purpose.**

Fencing

Fencing of some kind, preferably easily moved should be used to keep the birds within restricted areas. If there are serious problems with land becoming sour the answer may be to plough the field and re-sow with a quick growing grass. At one time regular liming was advocated, but a more specialised chemical to exterminate disease might be appropriate.

Lighting Patterns

The use of lights to give the required lighting pattern (e.g. 14 hours per day) will also be essential or egg numbers will not be maximised. Stocking should be realistic, but some producers attempt to house at the rate of 10 birds per square metre which may be regarded as too high in most situations; a figure of 5 is more realistic. Regular change of ground or some form of corrective action such as rotovating is essential and excessive stocking only aggravates the position. Obviously coping with high rates of stocking calls for efficient stockmanship and management.

Giving adequate lighting and controlling to the correct length of time is at variance with free-range poultry keeping; in fact, even without the difficulties of operation, questions may be raised on whether fowls should be stimulated into lay by artificial light unless kept intensively.

Egg Sterilizing

If eggs are to be clean and fresh there should be regular collections and if on a large scale a conveyor system will be necessary, thus minimising the handling costs. Washing facilities for eggs will be essential (although frowned upon by many because of possible misuse contaminating the eggs) and this may be a sophisticated machine or a bucket-cleaner such as the well tried *Rotamaid* system. When eggs are to be hatched there should be *sanitization* by passing the eggs through a special cleaning machine thus avoiding many problems and diseases which arise from dirty eggs.

If eggs are to be eaten, whatever method is used, must be safe to the consumer. In the case of **hatching eggs**, because of likely contamination becoming 'alive' in the incubation process, it will be necessary to use a solution which kills bacteria, but not the embryo. In a large scale operation a chemical known as *formalin* which is a fumigating agent, may be used, but only by a person with the appropriate knowledge and experience. This is also used to sterilize incubators after use, especially when there have been health problems. For further details of health hazards and procedures readers should refer to *Poultry Diseases Under Modern Management*, G S Coutts.

A Fold System

This may be adapted for Guineas, especially for rearing. Breeders are better with more space.

CLIPPING WINGS

When Guinea fowl are running out of doors and it is desirable to keep them from flying over the barrier fences the wings may be clipped or 'brailled' (a strap secures the wing feathers). It is advisable to perform only on one wing, thus affecting the balance of the bird. If both wings are clipped it will not be long before the bird will fly again.

FOLD UNITS

Fold Units are small units consisting of a house at one end and a wire netting covered run at the other (or in the middle). They are easily moved around so that a fresh patch of ground can be used when grass becomes eaten or soiled.

Construction

Folds should be movable on wheels or skids. Sometimes handles are placed at each end. Obviously folds should be robust, but quite light.

In a typical unit there is sufficient room for 20 birds. More than this number is not to be recommended.

Provision must be made for water and food containers and these must be under cover or the feed will be affected by inclement weather. This covered area can be at the opposite end of the sleeping compartment.

Practicability

Fold units are excellent for rearing chicks and growing stock. They may also be used for layers , broilers and Guinea Fowl.

The main **disadvantages** are:

(a)   **Fairly high capital cost to build the units;**

(b)   **High labour costs to supply food and water and collect eggs.**

A full-time poultryman would be required to look after around 1,500 birds, but more or less depending upon circumstances. Each one has to be supplied with food and water and usually there is difficulty in introducing an automatic system.

The usual recommended stock intensity **at maximum** is not more than 200 per acre and this would require many fold units. However, it appears obvious that anyone requiring to keep large numbers of birds should think of one of the other systems.

VERANDAHS / SLATTED FLOORS

A variation of the fold unit is the **raised** verandah where birds are kept on wire or slatted floors. The advantage of the method is a plentiful supply of fresh air with the avoidance of any birds being given direct access to the ground, which avoids disease.

The conventional slatted or twilweld floor allows birds to go indoors to roost , lay and shelter, but with automatic clearance of the droppings, which fall underneath the unit and can be removed quite easily.

The **pole barn** or **aviary** is also very suitable for Guinea fowl because it allows freedom of movement by the provision of high perches and an open front for ventilation.

SPECIAL HOUSES

Many new ideas have been put forward for poultry houses, the idea being to try to automate as far as possible, yet with the advantage of access to grass and fresh air.

One of the first priorities is attention to labour saving methods so that wages are minimised. Possible areas of attention are:

1. Ease of Cleaning

Slatted floors (or twilweld) allow droppings to fall through and, therefore, save labour. If contained in a compartment underneath the slats the ground is not fouled with the droppings, although after a time, if movement is necessary, there is a disadvantage in that the unit becomes quite heavy (regular clearance is therefore advised).

2. Water

Filling individual water fountains each day can be time consuming chore and, therefore, a header tank or something similar is desirable. Automatic drinkers would be essential for an intensive system. Failing that it is advisable to use a piped supply; a hose pipe can give great fexibility, but can cause problems in frosty weather.

3. Foodstuffs

As for water – some form of automatic feeding is desirable. As a minimum a large hopper would be essential, with a self-filling principle. Grit must also be given. For Guinea fowl small pellets or 'crumbles' should be used. Meal is not very palatable and large pellets are difficult to swallow.

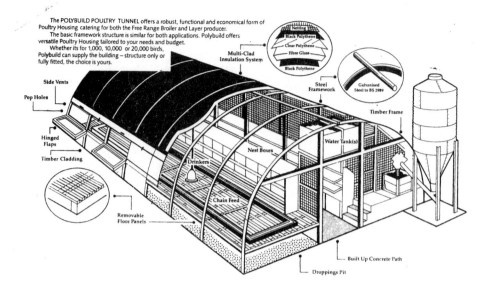

The POLYBUILD POULTRY TUNNEL offers a robust, functional and economical form of Poultry Housing catering for both the Free Range Broiler and Layer producer.
The basic framework structure is similar for both applications. Polybuild offers versatile Poultry Housing tailored to your needs and budget.
Whether its for 1,000, 10,000 or 20,000 birds, Polybuild can supply the building – structure only or fully fitted, the choice is yours.

Multi-Clad Insulation System

Netting
Black Polythene
Clear Polythene
Fibre Glass
Black Polythene

Steel Framework

Galvanised Steel to BS 2989

Side Vents

Pop Holes

Timber Frame

Hinged Flaps

Timber Cladding

Water Tank(s)

Nest Boxes

Drinkers

Chain Feed

Removable Floor Panels

Built Up Concrete Path

Droppings Pit

The *POLYBUILD* Poultry House for free range or other systems .(Pays great attention to insulation and will house 1000– upwards) **Courtesy: Polybuild**

A Free Range House for 250 layers The *Skidder* is moved on skids.
Courtesy:John Price & Son

EXAMPLES OF SHEDS AND LAYOUTS

A number of illustrations are given to show the types of houses and layouts that are found in practice. Some of these are from the days when free-range was a very popular system, before being replaced by laying batteries. Accordingly, they will serve as a guide to those who seek to establish free range. Although developed for standard type poultry, they can be used for Guinea Fowl.

The *Polybuild* concept attempts to give full automation within a single building. This is flexible and is a fully insulated building. Obviously, like all free range houses, it will be necessary to allow sufficient ground area for the birds to have a regular supply of grass. "Burnt up" patches and fouled ground have to be avoided but this should not be difficult if the house is placed in a convenient spot.

Where a movable house is preferred there is the Skidder, a unit 10ft X 6ft which may hold up to 300 birds. Obviously, the spacing of perches should be given attention and the Guineas must be brought up on the system or there will be difficulty in getting them to return each evening to roost. When first transferred into the house keep them inside for at least 3 weeks until they accustom themselves to the food and water.

CONCLUSION

There is much to be done to develop the potential of Guinea fowl. They have much to offer in terms of food potential. With their light frames and propensity to fatten quite well the possibilities are tremendous.

The natural environment is Free Range because they are semi-wild birds which thrive well outdoors. Moreover, the gamey flavour is retained; there is no question of producing something which, at its worst, is like eating cardboard.

The fact remains that intensive systems have been successful. In France the Guinea fowl is produced in large numbers on this basis, including the cage method. In Britain there are a few large producers and in the USA various schemes are in operation, although it would appear that free range is the preferred system.

There seems little doubt that the Guinea fowl will attract more attention. Outdoors they can find a great deal of their food so what better for those who have the facilities for keeping them.

INDEX